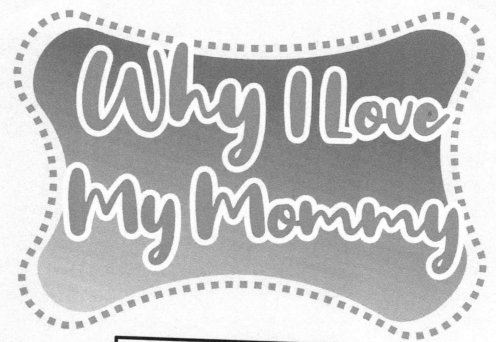

Why I Love My Mommy

COLORING BOOK

This book belongs to :

....

Written By Calandra and Emorii Stephens

Illustrated and Designed by ArtDan

Printed in the United States of America

Dedication

This book is dedicated to
Cailee, Reign, and Taigen.

I love my mommy
because she combs
my hair in pretty styles.

I love my mommy
because she listens to me.

I love my mommy because she protects me from the monsters under my bed.

3

I love my mommy because she let me play dress up in her makeup.

4

I love my mommy because
she buys me ice cream.

I love my mommy
because she taught me
how to tie my shoes.

I love my mommy because she taught me my ABC's and 123's.

7

I love my mommy
because she taught me
how to recite The Lord's Prayer.

I love my mommy because she wipes my tears away.

I love my mommy because she watches my favorite cartoons with me.

I love my mommy because when I'm scared to go to school, she tells me it will be okay.

I love my mommy
because she teaches me
how to cook.

12

I love my mommy
because she helps me
with my homework.

14

I love my mommy
because she reads me
a bedtime story and
tucks me in at night.

I love my mommy
because she is my mommy,
and she loves me.

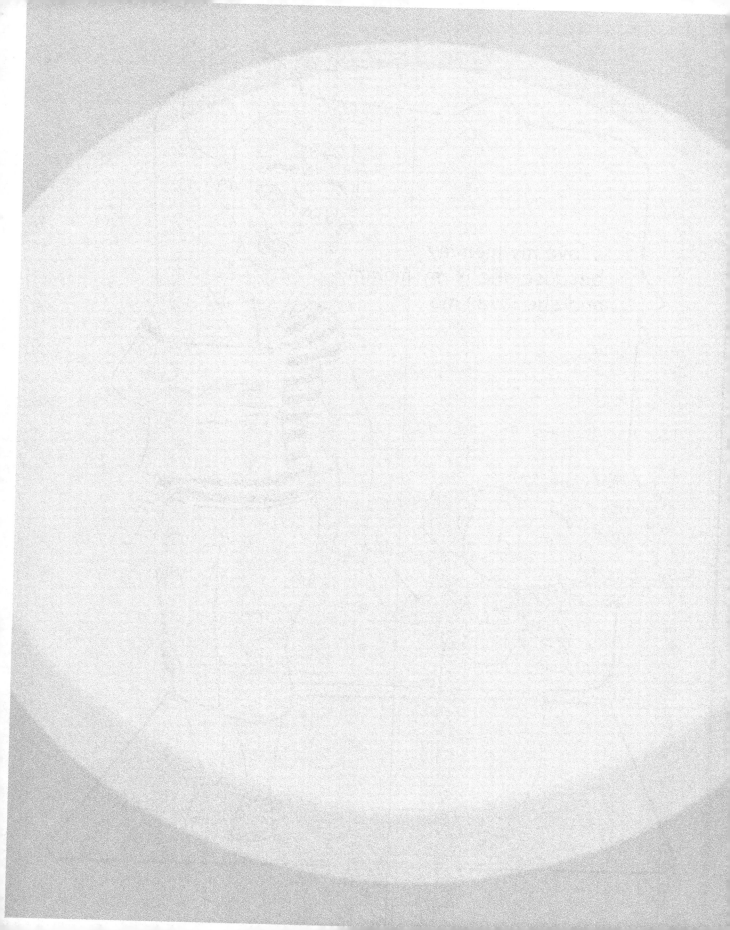

Lightning Source UK Ltd.
Milton Keynes UK
UKHW030642120421
381850UK00009B/966